We hope that you enjoy working through this book. You may find some pages quite easy and some quite hard but you are allowed to use counters or your fingers to help you. After lots of practice you won't need to use these as much because your memory will get better all the time.

Quick Additions

1   $12 + 5 =$
2   $11 + 9 =$
3   $18 + 4 =$
4   $16 + 9 =$
5   $14 + 5 =$
6   $15 + 8 =$
7   $12 + 7 =$
8   $19 + 9 =$
9   $22 + 6 =$
10 $27 + 8 =$

Quick Subtractions

1   $15 - 8 =$
2   $13 - 6 =$
3   $17 - 9 =$
4   $12 - 3 =$
5   $11 - 5 =$
6   $19 - 4 =$
7   $14 - 7 =$
8   $16 - 8 =$
9   $21 - 2 =$
10 $23 - 5 =$

Measurements

Remember:
  There are 100 centimetres in 1 metre.
  There are 50 centimetres in $\frac{1}{2}$ metre.

1   How many centimetres are there in 2 metres?

2   How many centimetres are there in 5 metres?

3   How many centimetres are there in 8 metres?

4   How many centimetres are there in 4 metres?

5   How many centimetres are there in $1\frac{1}{2}$ metres?

6   How many centimetres are there in $3\frac{1}{2}$ metres?

7   How many centimetres are there in $7\frac{1}{2}$ metres?

8   How many centimetres are there in $9\frac{1}{2}$ metres?

9   How many centimetres are there in $\frac{1}{4}$ metre?

10 How many centimetres are there in $\frac{3}{4}$ metre?

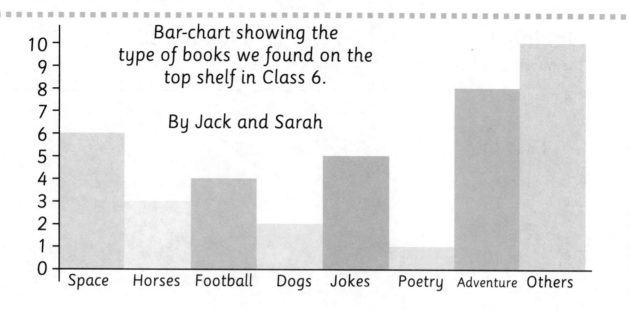

Bar-chart showing the type of books we found on the top shelf in Class 6.

By Jack and Sarah

1 How many books about football did Jack and Sarah find?

2 How many books about space did they find?

3 How many books about animals did they find?

4 How many more joke-books were there than poetry books?

5 What was the total number of space and adventure books?

6 How many fewer books were there about dogs than about horses?

7 Altogether, how many books were there about space, horses, football and dogs?

8 Altogether, how many books were there about jokes, poetry and adventure?

9 How many books were there on the top shelf altogether?

Making 10

Fill in the missing numbers:

1 $6 + \boxed{} = 10$
2 $3 + \boxed{} = 10$
3 $\boxed{} + 4 = 10$
4 $8 + \boxed{} = 10$
5 $5 + \boxed{} = 10$
6 $\boxed{} + 9 = 10$
7 $7 + \boxed{} = 10$
8 $\boxed{} + 2 = 10$
9 $0 + \boxed{} = 10$
10 $\boxed{} + 3 = 10$
11 $\boxed{} + 6 = 10$
12 $1 + \boxed{} = 10$

Making 20

1 $12 + \boxed{} = 20$
2 $14 + \boxed{} = 20$
3 $17 + \boxed{} = 20$
4 $19 + \boxed{} = 20$
5 $13 + \boxed{} = 20$
6 $16 + \boxed{} = 20$
7 $18 + \boxed{} = 20$
8 $11 + \boxed{} = 20$
9 $15 + \boxed{} = 20$
10 $10 + \boxed{} = 20$

Making 30

$29 + 1 = 30$

$1 + 29 = 30$

1 + 29 and 29 + 1 are both equal to 30

$30 - 29 = 1$

$30 - 1 = 29$

Complete the number pairs which make 30:

1 $2 + \boxed{} = 30$
2 $\boxed{} + 2 = 30$
3 $3 + \boxed{} = 30$
4 $\boxed{} + 3 = 30$
5 $4 + \boxed{} = 30$
6 $\boxed{} + 4 = 30$

7 $5 + \boxed{} = 30$
8 $\boxed{} + 5 = 30$
9 $6 + \boxed{} = 30$
10 $\boxed{} + 6 = 30$
11 $7 + \boxed{} = 30$
12 $\boxed{} + 7 = 30$

13 $8 + \boxed{} = 30$
14 $\boxed{} + 8 = 30$
15 $9 + \boxed{} = 30$
16 $\boxed{} + 9 = 30$
17 $10 + \boxed{} = 30$
18 $\boxed{} + 10 = 30$

19 $11 + \boxed{} = 30$
20 $\boxed{} + 11 = 30$
21 $12 + \boxed{} = 30$
22 $\boxed{} + 12 = 30$
23 $13 + \boxed{} = 30$
24 $\boxed{} + 13 = 30$

25 $14 + \boxed{} = 30$
26 $\boxed{} + 14 = 30$
27 $15 + \boxed{} = 30$
28 $\boxed{} + 15 = 30$
29 $0 + \boxed{} = 30$
30 $\boxed{} + 0 = 30$

Making 60

Complete this sequence which goes up in fives:

| 0 | 5 | | 15 | | | 30 | | 40 | | | | 60 |

Look at this number line to 60:

0 1 2 3 4 5 6 7 8 **9 10** 11 12 13 14 15 16 17 18 19 **20** 21 22 23 24 25 26 27 28 29 **30** 31 32 33 34 35 36 37 38 39 **40** 41 42 43 44 45 46 47 48 49 **50** 51 52 53 54 55 56 57 58 59 **60**

| 55 | 5 |

$$55 + 5 = 60$$

| 5 | 55 |

$$5 + 55 = 60$$

Complete the number pairs which make 60:

1. 5 + ☐ = 60
2. ☐ + 5 = 60
3. 10+ ☐ = 60
4. ☐ +10 = 60
5. 15+ ☐ = 60
6. ☐ +15 = 60
7. 20+ ☐ = 60
8. ☐ +20 = 60

9. 25+ ☐ = 60
10. ☐ +25 = 60
11. 30+ ☐ = 60
12. ☐ +30 = 60
13. 35+ ☐ = 60
14. ☐ +35 = 60
15. 40+ ☐ = 60
16. ☐ +40 = 30

17. 45+ ☐ = 60
18. ☐ +45 = 60
19. 50+ ☐ = 60
20. ☐ +50 = 60
21. 55+ ☐ = 60
22. ☐ +55 = 60
23. 60+ ☐ = 60
24. ☐ +60 = 60

There are 60 minutes in 1 hour ...

... So 25 minutes to 3 is the same as 35 minutes past 2.

$$25 + 35 = 60$$

5

Quick Additions

Try to find the answers in less than 4 minutes:

1. $4 + 7 + 3 =$
2. $6 + 9 + 5 =$
3. $7 + 2 + 2 =$
4. $8 + 4 + 8 =$
5. $5 + 3 + 7 =$
6. $6 + 6 + 6 =$
7. $10 + 4 + 7 =$
8. $8 + 8 + 8 =$
9. $3 + 9 + 7 =$
10. $12 + 9 + 9 =$
11. $5 + 5 + 5 =$
12. $6 + 13 + 7 =$
13. $2 + 8 + 4 =$
14. $7 + 7 + 7 =$
15. $3 + 4 + 7 =$
16. $9 + 9 + 9 =$
17. $8 + 11 + 9 =$
18. $5 + 9 + 5 =$
19. $6 + 8 + 14 =$
20. $7 + 8 + 9 =$

Which number?

1. Which of these numbers is an odd number?   216 419 626 700

2. Which of these numbers is an even number?   800 377 489 163

3. Which of these numbers is 10 more than 191 ?   181 211 291 201

4. Which of these numbers is 10 less than 604 ?   594 504 614 624

5. Which of these numbers is nearest to 400 ?   298 389 409 398

6. Which of these numbers is double 25   40 50 60 70

7. Which of these numbers is $\frac{1}{2}$ of 250 ?   125 225 150 112

8. Which of these numbers is 100 more than 278 ?   288 388 488 378

9. Which of these numbers is 100 less than 802 ?   702 602 792 902

10. Which of these numbers is $\frac{1}{4}$ of 100 ?   30 35 25 32

11. Which of these numbers is $\frac{3}{4}$ of 100 ?   30 25 50 75

12. Which of these numbers is $\frac{1}{2}$ of 1000 ?   50 200 100 500

Making 100

Look at this number line to 100:

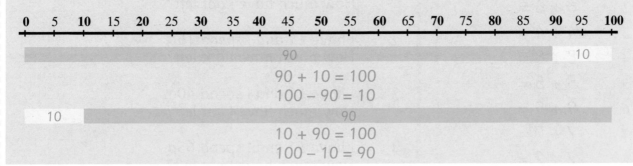

Fill in the missing numbers :

1 80 + [ ] = 100   3 30 + [ ] = 100   5 10 + [ ] = 100
2 [ ] + 60 = 100   4 [ ] + 50 = 100   6 [ ] + 70 = 100

7 100 − 40 = [ ]   9 100 − 20 = [ ]   11 100 − 10 = [ ]   13 100 − 70 = [ ]
8 100 − 30 = [ ]   10 100 − 90 = [ ]   12 100 − 60 = [ ]   14 100 − 80 = [ ]

45	55
45 + 55 = 100	55 + 45 = 100
100 − 45 = 55	100 − 55 = 45

Fill in the missing numbers :

15 95 + [ ] = 100   17 75 + [ ] = 100   19 5 + [ ] = 100
16 [ ] + 85 = 100   18 [ ] + 65 = 100   20 [ ] + 25 = 100

21 100 − 15 = [ ]   23 100 − 35 = [ ]   25 100 − 5 = [ ]   27 100 − 85 = [ ]
22 100 − 45 = [ ]   24 100 − 25 = [ ]   26 100 − 55 = [ ]   28 100 − 75 = [ ]

Quick Doubles

1. $3 + 3 =$
2. $6 + 6 =$
3. $4 + 4 =$
4. $8 + 8 =$
5. $5 + 5 =$
6. $9 + 9 =$
7. $7 + 7 =$
8. $2 + 2 =$
9. $11 + 11 =$
10. $14 + 14 =$
11. $12 + 12 =$
12. $15 + 15 =$

Quick Subtractions

1. $20 - 8 =$
2. $20 - 6 =$
3. $20 - 9 =$
4. $20 - 3 =$
5. $20 - 5 =$
6. $20 - 4 =$
7. $20 - 7 =$
8. $20 - 1 =$
9. $20 - 2 =$
10. $40 - 5 =$
11. $50 - 4 =$
12. $30 - 7 =$

Spending Money

1. I have £1 and I spend 30p. How much have I got left?
2. I have £1 and I spend 15p. How much have I got left?
3. I have £1 and I spend 40p. How much have I got left?
4. I have £1 and I spend 65p. How much have I got left?
5. I have £1 and I spend 45p. How much have I got left?
6. I have £1 and I spend 10p. How much have I got left?
7. I have £1 and I spend 35p. How much have I got left?
8. I have £1 and I spend 5p. How much have I got left?
9. I have £1 and I spend 90p. How much have I got left?
10. I have £1 and I spend 25p. How much have I got left?
11. I have £1 and I spend 55p. How much have I got left?
12. I have £1 and I spend 75p. How much have I got left?

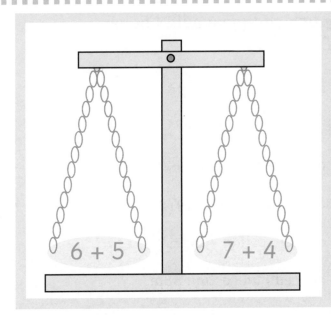

The scales are balanced because $6 + 5$ and $7 + 4$ are both equal to 11.

$$6 + 5 = 11 \qquad 7 + 4 = 11$$

so ...

$$6 + 5 = 7 + 4$$

Both sides of the equals sign must be worth the same.

Fill in the missing numbers to make both sides of the equals sign balance:

1 $8 + 5 = 9 + \boxed{}$

2 $\boxed{} + 7 = 9 + 2$

3 $5 + \boxed{} = 6 + 3$

4 $12 + 8 = 15 + \boxed{}$

5 $\boxed{} + 6 = 10 + 10$

6 $8 + \boxed{} = 7 + 9$

7 $16 + \boxed{} = 18 + 1$

8 $18 + \boxed{} = 9 + 9$

9 $9 + 7 = \boxed{} + 4$

10 $8 + 8 = \boxed{} + 1$

11 $17 + 2 = 10 + \boxed{}$

12 $12 + 8 = 13 + \boxed{}$

13 $11 + \boxed{} = 17 + 3$

14 $\boxed{} + 15 = 11 + 7$

15 $8 + 6 = 5 + \boxed{}$

16 $12 + 12 = 23 + \boxed{}$

17 $13 + 13 = \boxed{} + 4$

18 $14 + \boxed{} = 25 + 3$

Quick Numbers

1. $14 + 6 - 5 =$
2. $17 + 3 - 11 =$
3. $15 + 5 - 4 =$
4. $12 + 8 - 13 =$
5. $16 + 4 - 3 =$
6. $11 + 9 - 7 =$
7. $13 + 7 - 12 =$
8. $18 + 2 - 14 =$
9. $19 + 1 - 17 =$
10. $17 + 7 - 6 =$
11. $16 + 9 - 8 =$
12. $18 + 8 - 9 =$
13. $17 + 4 - 11 =$
14. $15 + 9 - 13 =$
15. $14 + 13 - 12 =$
16. $19 + 12 - 8 =$
17. $18 + 18 - 4 =$
18. $13 + 13 - 5 =$
19. $12 + 17 - 6 =$
20. $15 + 16 - 9 =$

How much change would I have from £1 if I buy ...

1. a rubber costing 60p?
2. a pencil costing 36p?
3. a sharpener costing 82p?
4. a notebook costing 47p?
5. a ruler costing 75p?
6. an iced bun costing 58p?
7. a small chocolate bar costing 34p?
8. a box of paper-clips costing 99p?
9. a newspaper costing 35p?
10. 2 pencils at 36p each?
11. 2 notebooks at 47p each?
12. 2 chocolate bars at 34p each?
13. 2 packs of stickers at 45p each?
14. a pencil for 36p and a rubber for 60p?
15. a pencil for 36p and a notebook for 47p?

Addition Square

Practise quick addition by completing this square.
Try to complete it in less than 3 minutes :

+	1	2	3	4	5	6	7	8	9	10	20	30
1	2				6							
2			5				9					
3												
4						10						
5												
6												
7				11								
8												
9										19		
10												
25												
50												

Add these sets of numbers as quickly as possible:

1 6 + 7 + 5 + 3 + 4 + 9 =

2 9 + 8 + 2 + 11 + 7 + 1 =

3 13 + 5 + 7 + 14 + 9 + 2 =

4 25 + 50 + 25 + 10 + 90 =

Quick Halves

1. $\frac{1}{2}$ of 10 =
2. $\frac{1}{2}$ of 100 =
3. $\frac{1}{2}$ of 1000 =
4. $\frac{1}{2}$ of 20 =
5. $\frac{1}{2}$ of 40 =
6. $\frac{1}{2}$ of 30 =
7. $\frac{1}{2}$ of 18 =
8. $\frac{1}{2}$ of 14 =
9. $\frac{1}{2}$ of 24 =
10. $\frac{1}{2}$ of 50 =
11. $\frac{1}{2}$ of 80 =
12. $\frac{1}{2}$ of 16 =
13. $\frac{1}{2}$ of 90 =
14. $\frac{1}{2}$ of 60 =
15. $\frac{1}{2}$ of 32 =
16. $\frac{1}{2}$ of 70 =
17. $\frac{1}{2}$ of 500 =
18. $\frac{1}{2}$ of 300 =
19. $\frac{1}{2}$ of 400 =
20. $\frac{1}{2}$ of 600 =

If I have £2 pocket money...

1. ... how much will I have left if I buy a magazine for £1.75 ?

2. ... how much more do I need to buy a book for £2.99 ?

3. ... how much more do I need to buy a CD for £3.99 ?

4. ... how much change will I have if I buy a file for £1.20 ?

5. ... how much change will I have if I buy a stapler for £1.55 ?

6. ... how much change will I have if I buy 3 chocolate bars at 50p each?

7. ... how much change will I have if I buy a chew-sweet for 8p?

8. ... how much change will I have if I buy 10 of these chew-sweets?

If I have £1.50 pocket money each week...

9. ... for how many weeks will I need to save to buy a book for £3 ?

10. ... for how many weeks will I need to save to buy a CD case for £6 ?

Adding 9

A quick way to add 9 to another number
is to add 10 instead, then take away 1.
Look:

$$26 + 9 \longrightarrow 26 + 10 = 36 \longrightarrow 36 - 1 = 35$$

$$\text{So} \quad 26 + 9 = 35$$

Find the answers to these questions:

1 83 + 9 =	5 46 + 9 =	9 39 + 9 =	13 71 + 9 =
2 22 + 9 =	6 8 + 9 =	10 64 + 9 =	14 55 + 9 =
3 11 + 9 =	7 61 + 9 =	11 99 + 9 =	15 27 + 9 =
4 162 + 9 =	8 273 + 9 =	12 347 + 9 =	16 280 + 9 =

To add 19, just add 20, then subtract 1:

1 36 + 19 =	4 46 + 19 =	7 39 + 19 =	10 71 + 19 =
2 22 + 19 =	5 8 + 19 =	8 64 + 19 =	11 55 + 19 =
3 11 + 19 =	6 61 + 19 =	9 99 + 19 =	12 27 + 19 =

Solve these 2 times tables questions as quickly as you can:

1   6 x 2 =
2   10 ÷ 2 =
3   9 x 2 =
4   6 ÷ 2 =
5   18 ÷ 2 =
6   4 x 2 =
7   7 x 2 =
8   2 x 2 =
9   20 ÷ 2 =
10   0 x 2 =
11   16 ÷ 2 =
12   14 ÷ 2 =
13   8 x 2 =
14   3 x 2 =
15   4 ÷ 2 =
16   5 x 2 =
17   1 x 2 =
18   2 ÷ 2 =
19   8 ÷ 2 =
20   12 ÷ 2 =

Beat the clock!

Work as fast as you can.

Try to do all these questions in less than 90 seconds.

1   7 + 9 =
2   2 + 9 =
3   9 + 9 =
4   13 + 9 =
5   23 + 9 =
6   47 + 9 =
7   52 + 9 =
8   65 + 9 =
9   82 + 9 =
10   38 + 9 =
11   25 + 9 =
12   98 + 9 =
13   8 + 9 =
14   4 + 9 =
15   5 + 9 =
16   101 + 9 =

Try to do all these questions in less than 90 seconds.

1   20 – 6 =
2   20 – 11 =
3   20 – 4 =
4   20 – 8 =
5   20 – 18 =
6   20 – 12 =
7   20 – 5 =
8   20 – 9 =
9   20 – 1 =
10   20 – 17 =
11   20 – 14 =
12   20 – 7 =
13   20 – 10 =
14   20 – 13 =
15   20 – 2 =
16   20 – 15 =

Subtracting 9

A quick way to subtract 9 from another number
is to subtract 10 instead, then add 1 back on.
Look:

$$47 - 9 \longrightarrow 47 - 10 = 37 \longrightarrow 37 + 1 = 38$$

So $47 - 9 = 38$

Find the answers to these questions:

1 $54 - 9 =$	4 $68 - 9 =$	7 $82 - 9 =$	10 $96 - 9 =$
2 $100 - 9 =$	5 $40 - 9 =$	8 $12 - 9 =$	11 $37 - 9 =$
3 $76 - 9 =$	6 $93 - 9 =$	9 $21 - 9 =$	12 $85 - 9 =$

These number sequences go up in nines.
Fill in the missing answers:

13   $\boxed{}$ $\boxed{7}$ $\boxed{16}$ $\boxed{}$ $\boxed{}$ $\boxed{43}$ $\boxed{52}$ $\boxed{}$ $\boxed{}$

14 $-\ 3\ -\ 12\ -\ \bigcirc\ -\ 30\ -\ \bigcirc\ -\ \bigcirc\ -\ 57\ -\ 66\ -\ \bigcirc\ -$

These number sequences go down in nines:

15 $\boxed{90}$ $\boxed{}$ $\boxed{72}$ $\boxed{}$ $\boxed{54}$ $\boxed{}$ $\boxed{36}$ $\boxed{}$ $\boxed{18}$ $\boxed{9}$ $\boxed{}$

16 $-\ 100\ -\ \bigcirc\ -\ 82\ -\ \bigcirc\ -\ 64\ -\ 55\ -\ \bigcirc\ -\ 37\ -\ \bigcirc\ -\ 19\ -$

Solve these 3 times tables questions as quickly as you can:

1 2 x 3 =

2 0 x 3 =

3 12 ÷ 3 =

4 8 x 3 =

5 18 ÷ 3 =

6 5 x 3 =

7 21 ÷ 3 =

8 4 x 3 =

9 30 ÷ 3 =

10 9 x 3 =

11 9 ÷ 3 =

12 1 x 3 =

13 15 ÷ 3 =

14 3 x 3 =

15 24 ÷ 3 =

16 6 x 3 =

17 3 ÷ 3 =

18 7 x 3 =

19 6 ÷ 3 =

20 27 ÷ 3 =

Words and numbers

Match the words to the numbers.
The first one is done for you.

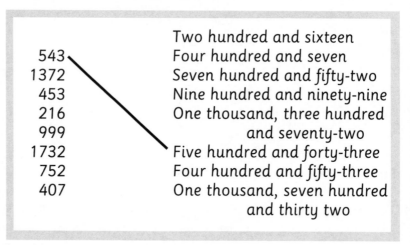

543	Two hundred and sixteen
1372	Four hundred and seven
453	Seven hundred and fifty-two
216	Nine hundred and ninety-nine
999	One thousand, three hundred and seventy-two
1732	Five hundred and forty-three
752	Four hundred and fifty-three
407	One thousand, seven hundred and thirty two

Write the words for the numbers:

1 219

2 647

3 1038

4 2475

5 7854

6 9562

7 8121

8 4786

Removable Answer Section

+	1	2	3	4	5	6	7	8	9	10	20	30
1	2	3	4	5	6	7	8	9	10	11	21	31
2	3	4	5	6	7	8	9	10	11	12	22	32
3	4	5	6	7	8	9	10	11	12	13	23	33
4	5	6	7	8	9	10	11	12	13	14	24	34
5	6	7	8	9	10	11	12	13	14	15	25	35
6	7	8	9	10	11	12	13	14	15	16	26	36
7	8	9	10	11	12	13	14	15	16	17	27	37
8	9	10	11	12	13	14	15	16	17	18	28	38
9	10	11	12	13	14	15	16	17	18	19	29	39
10	11	12	13	14	15	16	17	18	19	20	30	40
25	26	27	28	29	30	31	32	33	34	35	45	55
50	51	52	53	54	55	56	57	58	59	60	70	80

Page 11
Addition Questions

1 **34**

2 **38**

3 **50**

4 **200**

Page 12 Quick Halves

1 **5** 2 **50** 3 **500** 4 **10** 5 **20** 6 **15** 7 **9** 8 **7** 9 **12** 10 **25** 11 **40** 12 **8**
13 **45** 14 **30** 15 **16** 16 **35** 17 **250** 18 **150** 19 **200** 20 **300**

Page 12 Pocket Money

1 **25p** 2 **99p** 3 **£1·99** 4 **80p** 5 **45p** 6 **50p** 7 **£1·92** 8 **£1·20** 9 **2 weeks** 10 **4 weeks**

Page 13 Adding 9

1 **92** 2 **31** 3 **20** 4 **171** 5 **55** 6 **17** 7 **70** 8 **282** 9 **48** 10 **73** 11 **108** 12 **356**
13 **80** 14 **64** 15 **36** 16 **289**

Page 13 Adding 19

1 **55** 2 **41** 3 **30** 4 **65** 5 **27** 6 **80** 7 **58** 8 **83** 9 **118** 10 **90** 11 **74** 12 **46**

Page 14 2 x table

1 **12** 2 **5** 3 **18** 4 **3** 5 **9** 6 **8** 7 **14** 8 **4** 9 **10** 10 **0** 11 **8** 12 **7** 13 **16** 14 **6** 15 **2** 16 **10** 17 **2** 18 **1** 19 **4** 20 **6**

Page 14 Beat the clock: additions

1 **16** 2 **11** 3 **18** 4 **22** 5 **32** 6 **56** 7 **61** 8 **74** 9 **91** 10 **47** 11 **34** 12 **107** 13 **17** 14 **13** 15 **14** 16 **110**

Page 14 Beat the clock: subtractions
1 14   2 9   3 16   4 12   5 2   6 8   7 15   8 11   9 19   10 3   11 6   12 13   13 10   14 7   15 18   16 5

Page 15
1 45   2 91   3 67   4 59   5 31   6 84   7 73   8 3   9 12   10 87   11 28   12 76
13 25, 34, 61, 70   14 21, 39, 48, 75   15 81, 63, 45, 27, 0   16 91, 73, 46, 28

Page 16 3 x table
1 6   2 0   3 4   4 24   5 6   6 15   7 7   8 12   9 10   10 27   11 3   12 3   13 5   14 9   15 8   16 18   17 1   18 21   19 2   20 9

Page 16
543 — One thousand, seven hundred and thirty two
1372 — Four hundred and fifty-three
453 — Five hundred and forty-three
216 — Two hundred and sixteen
999 — Nine hundred and ninety-nine
1732 — One thousand, three hundred and seventy-two
752 — Seven hundred and fifty-two
407 — Four hundred and seven

Page 16
1 two hundred and nineteen
2 six hundred and forty-seven
3 one thousand and thirty-eight
4 two thousand, four hundred and seventy-five
5 seven thousand, eight hundred and fifty-four
6 nine thousand, five hundred and sixty-two
7 eight thousand, one hundred and twenty-one
8 four thousand, seven hundred and eighty-six

Page 17
2 five past four   4.05   3 quarter past two   2.15   4 twenty past ten   10.20   5 ten past eight   8.10
6 half past nine   9.30   7 five past one   1.05   8 twenty-five past six   6.25   9 ten past seven   7.10

Page 18 4 x table
1 0   2 1   3 32   4 6   5 12   6 2   7 28   8 5   9 8   10 8   11 16   12 3   13 20   14 7   15 4   16 4   17 24   18 36   19 10   20 9

Page 18 Mixed Maths
1 25   2 500   3 28   4 7   5 17   6 13p   7 25p   8 57   9 50   10 130   11 12   12 18p   13 3   14 5   15 25

Page 19
1 twenty-five to nine   8.35   2 ten to four   3.50   3 five to eleven   10.55
4 twenty to five   4.40   5 quarter to eight   7.45   6 twenty-five to one   12.35

Page 20 5 x table
1 25   2 7   3 10   4 4   5 45   6 3   7 0   8 6   9 20   10 9   11 40   12 2   13 15   14 10   15 30   16 1   17 35   18 5   19 5   20 8

Page 20 Mixed Maths
1 £1·40   2 60p   3 £1·12   4 38p   5 60   6 3   7 300g   8 150g   9 4.20   10 $1\frac{1}{2}$ hours or 1 hour 30 minutes   11 £3·50

Page 21
1 10, 5   2 2, 1   3 4, 2   4 8, 4

Page 22 10 x table
1 10   2 8   3 60   4 10   5 30   6 4   7 90   8 7   9 0   10 2   11 50   12 6   13 80   14 1   15 20   16 3   17 40   18 5   19 70   20 9

Page 22 Halves and quarters
1 20, 10   2 16, 8   3 18   4 9   5 12   6 6   7 14   8 7   9 50   10 25   11 100   12 50   13 500   14 250   15 22   16 11   17 34   18 17

Page 23
1 25cm   2 25cm   3 110ml   4 368ml   5 6   6 36 minutes   7 £4·50   8 8.55 or five to nine   9 125m   10 £1·01

Page 24 Quick Doubles
1 16   2 6   3 14   4 8   5 18   6 24   7 10   8 26   9 40   10 30

Page 24 Quick Halves
1 4   2 $1\frac{1}{2}$ 3 $3\frac{1}{2}$ 4 2   5 $4\frac{1}{2}$ 6 6   7 $2\frac{1}{2}$ 8 $6\frac{1}{2}$ 9 10   10 $7\frac{1}{2}$

Page 24 Beat the clock, 1st section
1 14 2 14 3 21 4 7 5 6 6 8 7 18 8 13 9 39 10 8 11 12 12 24 13 24 14 32 15 28 16 26

Page 24 Beat the clock, 2nd section
1 11 2 21 3 29 4 18 5 6 6 36 7 29 8 7 9 7 10 19 11 30 12 30 13 21 14 12

Page 25 1st section: all the answers are 10

Page 25 2nd section
1 15 2 14 3 19 4 18 5 17 6 17 7 18 8 24 9 18 10 25 11 17 12 17 13 20 14 17 15 21 16 30 17 28 18 42 19 43 20 50

Page 26 Quick Balances
1 5 2 0 3 4 4 20 5 1 6 4 7 7 8 2 9 8 10 6 11 3 12 7 13 4 14 4 15 8

Page 26 Approximating to ten
1 40 2 60 3 90 4 40 5 10 6 20 7 20 8 50 9 10 10 20 11 30 12 40
13 50 14 60 15 70 16 80 17 90 18 100 19 250 20 620

Page 27

1 0	2 9	3 0	4 6	5 0	6 8	7 0	8 10
6	2	7	1	8	3	9	7
12	0	14	9	16	0	18	5
18	4	21	3	24	9	27	1
24	7	28	10	32	2	36	3
30	1	35	5	40	4	45	0
36	10	42	7	48	6	54	8
42	3	49	4	56	1	63	2
48	5	56	2	64	10	72	6
54	8	63	8	72	5	81	4
60	6	70	0	80	7	90	9

Page 28 Quick Multiplications
1 42 2 32 3 45 4 18 5 56 6 81
7 80 8 49 9 48 10 72 11 42 12 64

Quick Divisions
1 8 2 9 3 9 4 9 5 8 6 8
7 7 8 9 9 8 10 10 11 7 12 6

Measurements 1 500g 2 250g 3 2000g 4 3500g 5 1250g
6 500ml 7 250ml 8 3000ml 9 4500ml 10 2250ml

Page 29 1 60 2 230 3 590 4 1680 5 3150 6 840 7 8 8 4
9 36 10 89 11 67 12 124 13 700 14 200 15 900 16 1800 17 3800
18 4300 19 9400 20 34200 21 2000

Page 30 Change from £1
1 31p 2 68p 3 53p 4 75p 5 25p 6 20p 7 1p 8 92p 9 49p 10 51p

Page 30 Change from £2
1 54p 2 7p 3 42p 4 56p 5 30p 6 81p 7 £1·12 8 £1·38 9 50p 10 68p

Page 30 Numbers in order
1 11, 29, 47, 63, 72, 98   2 164, 239, 392, 416, 614, 923   3 257, 275, 527, 572, 725, 752
4 249, 294, 429, 492, 924, 942   5 $2\frac{1}{2}$, 3, 4, 6, $6\frac{1}{2}$, $9\frac{1}{2}$ 6 $3\frac{1}{2}$, 7, 9, $12\frac{1}{2}$, $15\frac{1}{2}$, 18
7 $\frac{1}{4}$, $\frac{1}{2}$, $\frac{3}{4}$, 1, $1\frac{1}{4}$, $1\frac{1}{2}$ 8 $1\frac{1}{4}$, $1\frac{1}{2}$, $2\frac{1}{4}$, $2\frac{1}{2}$, $2\frac{3}{4}$, $3\frac{1}{4}$

Page 31
1 14, 18, 24, 28, 30   2 25, 35, 40, 50, 60   3 20, 26, 29, 35, 41   4 100, 150, 225   5 $2\frac{1}{2}$, 4, 5, $5\frac{1}{2}$
6 $2\frac{1}{2}$, $2\frac{3}{4}$ 7 24, 16, 8, 4, 0   8 34, 30, 26, 24, 20   9 17, 19

Page 32 A 1 25 2 32 3 17 4 56 5 61 6 174 7 47 8 84 9 105 10 43 11 70 12 98 13 61 14 50 15 103

B 1 55p 2 62p 3 25p 4 11p 5 3p 6 20p 7 79p 8 41p 9 38p 10 87p 11 54p 12 46p 13 70p 14 75p 15 50p

C 1 27 2 36 3 56 4 28 5 18 6 18 7 40 8 49 9 54 10 48 11 80 12 81 13 42 14 35 15 64

D 1 7 2 3 3 9 4 7 5 5 6 4 7 8 8 8 9 9 10 6 11 5 12 4 13 6 14 6 15 8

What time is it?

Write the times shown on these clocks in two different ways.
The first one is done for you.

1

twenty-five past three

3.25

2

3

4

5

6

7

8

9

Solve these 4 times tables questions as quickly as you can:

1. $0 \times 4 =$
2. $4 \div 4 =$
3. $8 \times 4 =$
4. $24 \div 4 =$
5. $3 \times 4 =$
6. $8 \div 4 =$
7. $7 \times 4 =$
8. $20 \div 4 =$
9. $2 \times 4 =$
10. $32 \div 4 =$
11. $4 \times 4 =$
12. $12 \div 4 =$
13. $5 \times 4 =$
14. $28 \div 4 =$
15. $1 \times 4 =$
16. $16 \div 4 =$
17. $6 \times 4 =$
18. $9 \times 4 =$
19. $40 \div 4 =$
20. $36 \div 4 =$

Mixed Maths

1. What number is half of 50 ?

2. What number is half of 1000 ?

3. What is the total of 18, 6 and 4 ?

4. What number is added to 13 to make 20 ?

5. What number is added to 13 to make 30 ?

6. By how much is 50p more than 37p?

7. How much more than 75p is £1 ?

8. How much should I add to 43 to make 100 ?

9. What number is double 25 ?

10. What is the sum of 52, 48 and 30 ?

11. What is the difference between 25 and 37 ?

12. How much less than 60p is 42p?

13. What number is $\frac{1}{4}$ of 12 ?

14. What number is $\frac{1}{4}$ of 20 ?

15. What number is $\frac{1}{4}$ of 100 ?

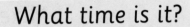

What time is it?

This clock shows the time
10 minutes to 6 o' clock.
(We normally say 'ten to six').
This is the same time as 50
minutes after 5 o' clock.
So we can write the time in two ways:

Ten to six
or
5.50

Write the times shown on these clocks in two different ways:

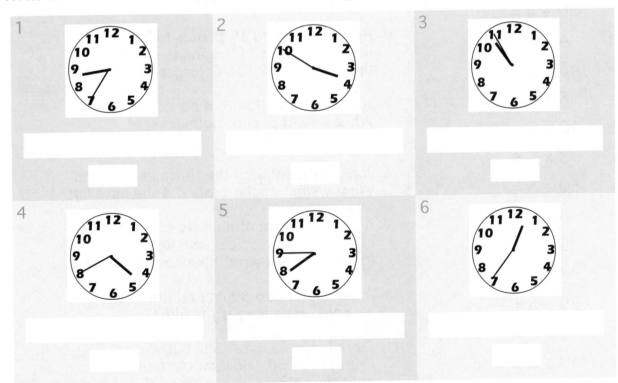

Answer these 5 times tables questions in less than 2 minutes:

1. $5 \times 5 =$
2. $35 \div 5 =$
3. $2 \times 5 =$
4. $20 \div 5 =$
5. $9 \times 5 =$
6. $15 \div 5 =$
7. $0 \times 5 =$
8. $30 \div 5 =$
9. $4 \times 5 =$
10. $45 \div 5 =$
11. $8 \times 5 =$
12. $10 \div 5 =$
13. $3 \times 5 =$
14. $50 \div 5 =$
15. $6 \times 5 =$
16. $5 \div 5 =$
17. $7 \times 5 =$
18. $25 \div 5 =$
19. $1 \times 5 =$
20. $40 \div 5 =$

Mixed Maths

1. Eliza bought 2 postcards for 45p each and 2 stamps for 25p each. How much did she spend?

2. How much change did Eliza have from £2 ?

3. Tristan bought 4 kiwi fruits for 28p each. How much did they cost altogether?

4. If Tristan had £1.50 to start with, How much did he have left?

5. Lemonade is on sale in packs of 15 cans. Holly buys four packs. How many cans does she have altogether?

6. Holly has invited 19 friends to her party. How many cans of lemonade could they have each? (Don't forget Holly)

7. Jan bought 3 100-gram bars of chocolate. What weight of chocolate did she have altogether?

8. Jan gave away half the chocolate she had. What weight of chocolate did she have left?

9. A television programme starts at five minutes to four o'clock and lasts for 25 minutes. At what time does it finish?

10. A film starts at 6.30pm and finishes at 8pm. How long is the film?

11. Clare has a £5 note. She buys some chips for £1.50. How much change does she get?

Finding halves and quarters

To find $\frac{1}{4}$ of a number, we can divide by 4
    Find $\frac{1}{4}$ of 12:

$$12 \div 4 = 3 \quad \text{so} \quad \frac{1}{4} \text{ of } 12 = 3$$

Another way to find $\frac{1}{4}$:

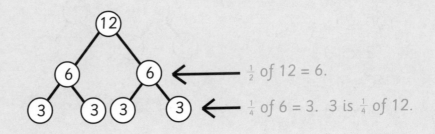

$\frac{1}{2}$ of 12 = 6.

$\frac{1}{4}$ of 6 = 3. 3 is $\frac{1}{4}$ of 12.

Find the missing numbers:

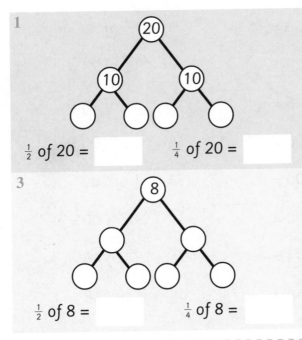

1

$\frac{1}{2}$ of 20 = ☐ $\frac{1}{4}$ of 20 = ☐

2

$\frac{1}{2}$ of 4 = ☐ $\frac{1}{4}$ of 4 = ☐

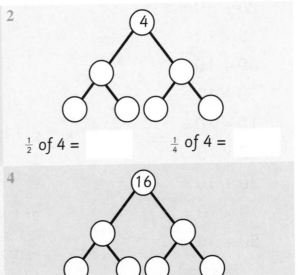

3

$\frac{1}{2}$ of 8 = ☐ $\frac{1}{4}$ of 8 = ☐

4

$\frac{1}{2}$ of 16 = ☐ $\frac{1}{4}$ of 16 = ☐

21

Answer these 10 times table questions in less than 90 seconds:

1.   1 x 10 =
2.   80 ÷ 10 =
3.   6 x 10 =
4.   100 ÷ 10 =
5.   3 x 10 =
6.   40 ÷ 10 =
7.   9 x 10 =
8.   70 ÷ 10 =
9.   0 x 10 =
10.   20 ÷ 10 =
11.   5 x 10 =
12.   60 ÷ 10 =
13.   8 x 10 =
14.   10 ÷ 10 =
15.   2 x 10 =
16.   30 ÷ 10 =
17.   4 x 10 =
18.   50 ÷ 10 =
19.   7 x 10 =
20.   90 ÷ 10 =

More halves and quarters

Fill in the missing numbers:

1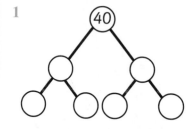

$\frac{1}{2}$ of 40 = ☐

$\frac{1}{4}$ of 40 = ☐

2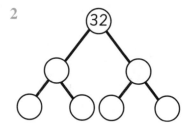

$\frac{1}{2}$ of 32 = ☐

$\frac{1}{4}$ of 32 = ☐

3   $\frac{1}{2}$ of 36 = ☐   4 $\frac{1}{4}$ of 36 = ☐

5   $\frac{1}{2}$ of 24 = ☐   6 $\frac{1}{4}$ of 24 = ☐

7   $\frac{1}{2}$ of 28 = ☐   8 $\frac{1}{4}$ of 28 = ☐

9   $\frac{1}{2}$ of 100 = ☐   10 $\frac{1}{4}$ of 100 = ☐

11   $\frac{1}{2}$ of 200 = ☐   12 $\frac{1}{4}$ of 200 = ☐

13   $\frac{1}{2}$ of 1000 = ☐   14 $\frac{1}{4}$ of 1000 = ☐

15   $\frac{1}{2}$ of 44 = ☐   16 $\frac{1}{4}$ of 44 = ☐

17   $\frac{1}{2}$ of 68 = ☐   18 $\frac{1}{4}$ of 68 = ☐

More number problems

1. Alex is 137 cm tall. Jenny is 112 cm tall.
   How much taller is Alex than Jenny?

2. Mike has a plank of wood which is 1metre long.
   He cuts it into four equal pieces. How long is each piece?

3. Becky has a bottle containing 125 millilitres of shampoo.
   She uses 15 millilitres to wash her hair.
   How much shampoo is left in the bottle?

4. There are 568 millilitres of milk in a carton.
   Tom uses 200 millilitres in his cooking.
   How much milk is left in the carton?

5. Caroline has a 3 hour video tape.
   How many programmes can she record on it,
   if each program is 30 minutes long?

6. Charlie is practising for a boat race.
   It takes her 12 minutes to row each kilometre.
   How long does it take her to row 3 kilometres?

7. Victoria has £1.50 pocket money every week.
   How much will she have altogether
   if she saves her pocket money for 3 weeks?

8. It takes Gemma 25 minutes to get to school.
   She leaves home at half past eight.
   What time does Gemma arrive at school?

9. Duncan swims 5 lengths of the swimming pool.
   The pool is 25 metres long.
   How far does Duncan swim altogether?

10. Richard has £5. He buys a CD for £3.99.
    How much has he got left?

Quick doubles

1. double 8 =
2. double 3 =
3. double 7 =
4. double 4 =
5. double 9 =
6. double 12 =
7. double 5 =
8. double 13 =
9. double 20 =
10. double 15 =

Quick halves

1. $\frac{1}{2}$ of 8 =
2. $\frac{1}{2}$ of 3 =
3. $\frac{1}{2}$ of 7 =
4. $\frac{1}{2}$ of 4 =
5. $\frac{1}{2}$ of 9 =
6. $\frac{1}{2}$ of 12 =
7. $\frac{1}{2}$ of 5 =
8. $\frac{1}{2}$ of 13 =
9. $\frac{1}{2}$ of 20 =
10. $\frac{1}{2}$ of 15 =

Beat the clock!

Work as fast as you can.

Try to do all these questions in less than 2 minutes.

1. 5 + 3 + 6 =
2. 2 + 4 + 8 =
3. 7 + 5 + 9 =
4. 6 + 4 − 3 =
5. 5 + 8 − 7 =
6. 9 + 4 − 5 =
7. 12 + 12 − 6 =
8. 9 + 9 − 5 =
9. 14 + 14 + 11 =
10. 7 + 7 − 6 =
11. 4 + 4 + 4 =
12. 13 + 6 + 5 =
13. 18 + 4 + 2 =
14. 17 + 9 + 6 =
15. 20 + 16 − 8 =
16. 21 + 14 − 9 =

Try to do all these questions in less than 3 minutes. Remember to do the part in brackets first.

1. (2 x 4) + 3 =
2. (3 x 5) + 6 =
3. (5 x 4) + 9 =
4. (8 x 3) − 6 =
5. (9 x 2) − 12 =
6. (7 x 4) + 8 =
7. (9 x 4) − 7 =
8. (4 x 3) − 5 =
9. (8 x 2) − 9 =
10. (4 x 4) + 3 =
11. (9 x 3) + 3 =
12. (10 x 2) + 10 =
13. (6 x 4) − 3 =
14. (7 x 3) − 9 =

Finding tens

Sometimes we can add sets of numbers quickly by findings pairs which make ten.

Look:

$6 + 3 + 4 \longrightarrow 6 + 3 + 4 = 6 + 4 + 3 = 10 + 3 = 13$

Find the answers to these questions:

1 $5 + 5 =$ ☐

2 $6 + 4 =$ ☐   4 $7 + 3 =$ ☐   6 $8 + 2 =$ ☐   8 $9 + 1 =$ ☐

3 $4 + 6 =$ ☐   5 $3 + 7 =$ ☐   7 $2 + 8 =$ ☐   9 $1 + 9 =$ ☐

Add these sets of numbers by finding pairs which make ten:

1 $7 + 5 + 3 =$ ☐   2 $8 + 2 + 4 =$ ☐   3 $3 + 9 + 7 =$ ☐

4 $8 + 1 + 9 =$ ☐   5 $5 + 7 + 5 =$ ☐   6 $6 + 7 + 4 =$ ☐

7 $3 + 6 + 2 + 7 =$ ☐   8 $6 + 5 + 4 + 9 =$ ☐   9 $5 + 8 + 3 + 2 =$ ☐

10 $8 + 7 + 1 + 9 =$ ☐   11 $5 + 2 + 3 + 7 =$ ☐   12 $6 + 2 + 5 + 4 =$ ☐

13 $7 + 5 + 3 + 5 =$ ☐   14 $3 + 9 + 4 + 1 =$ ☐   15 $2 + 4 + 7 + 8 =$ ☐

16 $6 + 3 + 9 + 7 + 4 + 1 =$ ☐   17 $2 + 3 + 9 + 5 + 8 + 1 =$ ☐

18 $6 + 7 + 2 + 4 + 8 + 3 + 12 =$ ☐   19 $11 + 8 + 3 + 2 + 9 + 4 + 6 =$ ☐

20 $9 + 22 + 6 + 8 + 1 + 4 =$ ☐

Quick balances

Fill in the missing numbers to make both sides balance.

1 6 + 7 = 18 – ☐

2 ☐ + 4 = 15 – 11

3 20 – 9 = 7 + ☐

4 8 + 7 = ☐ – 5

5 9 + 3 = 11 + ☐

6 20 – 14 = 10 – ☐

7 20 – 17 = 10 – ☐

8 20 – 12 = 10 – ☐

9 20 – 18 = 10 – ☐

10 10 + 4 = 20 – ☐

11 10 + 7 = 20 – ☐

12 10 + 3 = 20 – ☐

13 10 + 6 = 20 – ☐

14 12 + 12 = 20 + ☐

15 14 + 14 = 20 + ☐

Approximating to ten

Look:

The number 67 is between 60 and 70.
It is closest to 70.
We say that <u>67 rounded to the nearest 10</u> is 70

Round these numbers to the nearest ten:

1 39 → ☐   2 62 → ☐   3 88 → ☐

4 44 → ☐   5 6 → ☐   6 17 → ☐

7 21 → ☐   8 53 → ☐

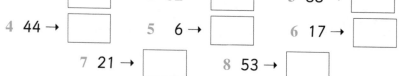

The number 45 is halfway between 40 and 50.
When a number is halfway
we always round <u>up</u> and not down...
...so <u>45 to the nearest ten</u> is 50.

Round these numbers to the nearest ten:

9 5 → ☐   10 15 → ☐   11 25 → ☐

12 35 → ☐   13 45 → ☐   14 55 → ☐

15 65 → ☐   16 75 → ☐   17 85 → ☐

18 95 → ☐   19 245 → ☐   20 619 → ☐

Multiplication tables

Fill in the missing answers:

1

0 x 6 =
1 x 6 =
2 x 6 =
3 x 6 =
4 x 6 =
5 x 6 =
6 x 6 =
7 x 6 =
8 x 6 =
9 x 6 =
10 x 6 =

2

54 ÷ 6 =
12 ÷ 6 =
0 ÷ 6 =
24 ÷ 6 =
42 ÷ 6 =
6 ÷ 6 =
60 ÷ 6 =
18 ÷ 6 =
30 ÷ 6 =
48 ÷ 6 =
36 ÷ 6 =

3

0 x 7 =
1 x 7 =
2 x 7 =
3 x 7 =
4 x 7 =
5 x 7 =
6 x 7 =
7 x 7 =
8 x 7 =
9 x 7 =
10 x 7 =

4

42 ÷ 7 =
7 ÷ 7 =
63 ÷ 7 =
21 ÷ 7 =
70 ÷ 7 =
35 ÷ 7 =
49 ÷ 7 =
28 ÷ 7 =
14 ÷ 7 =
56 ÷ 7 =
0 ÷ 7 =

5

0 x 8 =
1 x 8 =
2 x 8 =
3 x 8 =
4 x 8 =
5 x 8 =
6 x 8 =
7 x 8 =
8 x 8 =
9 x 8 =
10 x 8 =

6

64 ÷ 8 =
24 ÷ 8 =
0 ÷ 8 =
72 ÷ 8 =
16 ÷ 8 =
32 ÷ 8 =
48 ÷ 8 =
8 ÷ 8 =
80 ÷ 8 =
40 ÷ 8 =
56 ÷ 8 =

7

0 x 9 =
1 x 9 =
2 x 9 =
3 x 9 =
4 x 9 =
5 x 9 =
6 x 9 =
7 x 9 =
8 x 9 =
9 x 9 =
10 x 9 =

8

90 ÷ 9 =
63 ÷ 9 =
45 ÷ 9 =
9 ÷ 9 =
27 ÷ 9 =
0 ÷ 9 =
72 ÷ 9 =
18 ÷ 9 =
54 ÷ 9 =
36 ÷ 9 =
81 ÷ 9 =

Quick Multiplications

1. 6 x 7 =
2. 4 x 8 =
3. 5 x 9 =
4. 3 x 6 =
5. 8 x 7 =
6. 9 x 9 =
7. 10 x 8 =
8. 7 x 7 =
9. 6 x 8 =
10. 8 x 9 =
11. 7 x 6 =
12. 8 x 8 =

Quick Divisions

1. 72 ÷ 9 =
2. 63 ÷ 7 =
3. 54 ÷ 6 =
4. 81 ÷ 9 =
5. 64 ÷ 8 =
6. 48 ÷ 6 =
7. 49 ÷ 7 =
8. 72 ÷ 8 =
9. 56 ÷ 7 =
10. 90 ÷ 9 =
11. 63 ÷ 9 =
12. 48 ÷ 8 =

Measurements

There are 1000 grams in 1 kilogram

$$1000 \text{ g} = 1 \text{ kg}$$

1 How many grams are there in $\frac{1}{2}$ kg?

2 How many grams are there in $\frac{1}{4}$ kg?

3 How many grams are there in 2 kg?

4 How many grams are there in $3\frac{1}{2}$ kg?

5 How many grams are there in $1\frac{1}{4}$ kg?

There are 1000 millilitres in 1 litre

$$1000 \text{ ml} = 1 \text{ l}$$

6 How many millilitres are there in $\frac{1}{2}$ l?

7 How many millilitres are there in $\frac{1}{4}$ l?

8 How many millilitres are there in 3 l?

9 How many millilitres are there in $4\frac{1}{2}$ l?

10 How many millilitres are there in $2\frac{1}{4}$ l?

Multiplying by 10 or 100

Look:

$6 \times 10 = 60$

6 units .... multiplied by 10 .... moves the 6 into the tens column

$48 \times 10 = 480$

4 tens   8 units   4 hundreds and 8 tens

Fill in the missing numbers:

1 $6 \times 10 =$	2 $23 \times 10 =$	3 $59 \times 10 =$
4 $168 \times 10 =$	5 $315 \times 10 =$	6 $84 \times 10 =$
7 $\boxed{} \times 10 = 80$	8 $\boxed{} \times 10 = 40$	9 $\boxed{} \times 10 = 360$
10 $\boxed{} \times 10 = 890$	11 $\boxed{} \times 10 = 670$	12 $\boxed{} \times 10 = 1240$

Look:

$5 \times 100 = 500$

5 units .... multiplied by 100 .... moves the 5 into the hundreds column

13 $7 \times 100 =$	14 $2 \times 100 =$	15 $9 \times 100 =$
16 $18 \times 100 =$	17 $38 \times 100 =$	18 $43 \times 100 =$
19 $94 \times 100 =$	20 $342 \times 100 =$	21 $20 \times 100 =$

Change from £1

1. £1 – 69p =
2. £1 – 32p =
3. £1 – 47p =
4. £1 – 25p =
5. £1 – 75p =
6. £1 – 80p =
7. £1 – 99p =
8. £1 – 8p =
9. £1 – 51p =
10. £1 – 49p =

Change from £2

1. £2 – £1·46 =
2. £2 – £1·93 =
3. £2 – £1·58 =
4. £2 – £1·44 =
5. £2 – £1·70 =
6. £2 – £1·19 =
7. £2 – 88p =
8. £2 – 62p =
9. £2 – £1·50 =
10. £2 – £1·32 =

Numbers in order

Write each set of numbers in the correct order, starting with the smallest:

1. | 72 | 47 | 63 | 98 | 29 | 11 |
|---|---|---|---|---|---|
| | | | | | |

2. | 164 | 614 | 239 | 392 | 416 | 923 |
|---|---|---|---|---|---|
| | | | | | |

3. | 572 | 275 | 257 | 725 | 527 | 752 |
|---|---|---|---|---|---|
| | | | | | |

4. | 249 | 942 | 924 | 429 | 294 | 492 |
|---|---|---|---|---|---|
| | | | | | |

5. | $6\frac{1}{2}$ | 3 | $2\frac{1}{2}$ | 4 | $9\frac{1}{2}$ | 6 |
|---|---|---|---|---|---|
| | | | | | |

6. | 18 | 7 | $12\frac{1}{2}$ | $3\frac{1}{2}$ | 9 | $15\frac{1}{2}$ |
|---|---|---|---|---|---|
| | | | | | |

7. | 1 | $\frac{1}{2}$ | $1\frac{1}{4}$ | $\frac{3}{4}$ | $\frac{1}{4}$ | $1\frac{1}{2}$ |
|---|---|---|---|---|---|
| | | | | | |

8. | $2\frac{1}{2}$ | $1\frac{1}{4}$ | $3\frac{1}{4}$ | $2\frac{3}{4}$ | $1\frac{1}{2}$ | $2\frac{1}{4}$ |
|---|---|---|---|---|---|
| | | | | | |

Sequences of numbers

Write the missing numbers in the sequences below:

1. — 10 — 12 — ⬭ — 16 — ⬭ — 20 — 22 — ⬭ — 26 — ⬭ — ⬭ —

2. 10 ⬜ 15 ⬜ 20 ⬜ ⬜ 30 ⬜ ⬜ 45 ⬜ ⬜ 55

3. — 8 — 11 — 14 — 17 — ⬭ — 23 — ⬭ — ⬭ — 32 — ⬭ — 38 — ⬭ —

4. 25 ⬜ 50 ⬜ 75 ⬜ ⬜ 125 ⬜ ⬜ 175 ⬜ 200

5. — $\frac{1}{2}$ — 1 — $1\frac{1}{2}$ — 2 — ⬭ — 3 — $3\frac{1}{2}$ — ⬭ — $4\frac{1}{2}$ — ⬭ — ⬭ — 6 —

6. $\frac{1}{4}$ ⬜ $\frac{1}{2}$ ⬜ $\frac{3}{4}$ ⬜ 1 ⬜ $1\frac{1}{4}$ ⬜ $1\frac{1}{2}$ ⬜ $1\frac{3}{4}$ ⬜ 2 ⬜ $2\frac{1}{4}$ ⬜ ⬜ 3

7. — 32 — 28 — ⬭ — 20 — ⬭ — 12 — ⬭ — ⬭ — ⬭ —

8. 40 ⬜ 38 ⬜ 36 ⬜ ⬜ 32 ⬜ ⬜ 28 ⬜ ⬜ ⬜ 22

In the sequence below we add 1 then 2 then 1 again and so on:

9. — 7 — 8 — 10 — 11 — 13 — 14 — 16 — ⬭ — ⬭ —

31

Beat the clock!

Complete each section as fast as you can.

The tables opposite will help you with sections C and D.

A	B	C	D
Try to do these questions in less than 90 seconds.	Try to do these questions in less than 3 minutes.	Try to do these questions in less than 3 minutes.	Try to do these questions in less than 3 minutes.
1 16 + 9 =	1 £1 – 45p =	1 3 x 9 =	1 63 ÷ 9 =
2 23 + 9 =	2 £1 – 38p =	2 6 x 6 =	2 24 ÷ 8 =
3 8 + 9 =	3 £1 – 75p =	3 7 x 8 =	3 81 ÷ 9 =
4 47 + 9 =	4 £1 – 89p =	4 4 x 7 =	4 49 ÷ 7 =
5 52 + 9 =	5 £1 – 97p =	5 2 x 9 =	5 30 ÷ 6 =
6 165 + 9 =	6 £1 – 80p =	6 3 x 6 =	6 32 ÷ 8 =
7 38 + 9 =	7 £1 – 21p =	7 5 x 8 =	7 72 ÷ 9 =
8 75 + 9 =	8 £1 – 59p =	8 7 x 7 =	8 56 ÷ 7 =
9 96 + 9 =	9 £1 – 62p =	9 6 x 9 =	9 54 ÷ 6 =
10 54 + 9 =	10 £1 – 13p =	10 8 x 6 =	10 48 ÷ 8 =
11 61 + 9 =	11 £1 – 46p =	11 10 x 8 =	11 35 ÷ 7 =
12 89 + 9 =	12 £1 – 54p =	12 9 x 9 =	12 24 ÷ 6 =
13 42 + 19 =	13 £1 – 30p =	13 7 x 6 =	13 36 ÷ 6 =
14 31 + 19 =	14 £1 – 25p =	14 5 x 7 =	14 42 ÷ 7 =
15 84 + 19 =	15 £1 – 50p =	15 8 x 8 =	15 64 ÷ 8 =